GREAT
American Negroes
IN
VERSE
1723-1965

ELOISE CROSBY CULVER

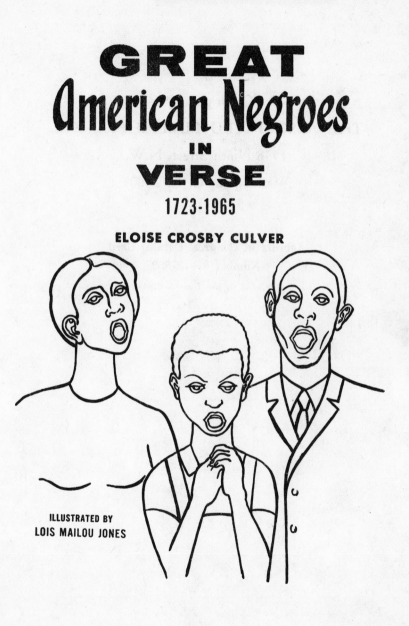

ILLUSTRATED BY
LOIS MAILOU JONES

©Copyright, 1966

THE ASSOCIATED PUBLISHERS, INC.

1538 Ninth Street, N.W.

Washington, D. C. 20001

Library of Congress Catalog Card
Number 65—27859

*Printed in the United States
of America*

Dedication

To all the young children it has been my privilege to guide and teach, especially my daughter, Deborah.

Author's Preface

Negro children in North America live in a land where most of the heroes are white. At home, as pre-schoolers, they look at pictures of Little Bo-Peep, Jack and the Beanstalk, or Mary and her Little Lamb, who is also white. Nowhere do they find images of themselves.

At school they learn of such great statesmen as George Washington and Abraham Lincoln, or such scientists as Thomas A. Edison and Albert Einstein. Still they find no self-image.

For entertainment they look at TV or go to the movies. Do they see any people like themselves? Is it any wonder that young Negroes may fail to develop a sense of pride in themselves?

This sense of pride could go far to eradicate the waste of juvenile delinquency and school drop-outs.

It is a sense of pride in their history that has made the Jewish people come through years of oppression with some of the most distinguished men in the world. Yet Negro children have many heroes and heroines with whom they might identify—if only they were placed before the children.

This we *must* do if Negro children are to develop a sense of self-worth and the inspiration to strive for greatness. If you don't believe it can happen, tell a small child about Dr. Charles A. Drew. Then show him a picture of this great man. Watch his shoulders straighten! Watch the interest in his eyes.

It is the same thing that happens to an adult when a person of his own ethnic or national group distinguishes himself. A little bit of that glory becomes a small but vibrant part of his innermost vital-force.

5

Shall we continue to frustrate little Negro children by giving them only heroes whom they can never see as images of themselves? And shall we continue to deprive white children of a fruitful knowledge of Negro Americans? Or shall we attempt to make a tardy, though sincere effort, to place before all of them the TOTAL HISTORY and achievement of ALL great men and women who have made our country a world leader?

Since we are all Americans, every child, not only the Negro one, is entitled to learn about all of the men and women who have written worthy chapters in the book of American History. Only then can all children enjoy that beauty which is Brotherhood!

For understanding, patience and encouragement, I am grateful to my husband, James, and to the following friends for their inspiring suggestions and helpful criticism: Mildred Bass, Langston Hughes, Oliver La Grone, Naomi Madgett, Necia Harkless Nembhard, Betty G. Patrick, Rosey E. Pool, and Charlemae Rollins.

ELOISE CROSBY CULVER

TABLE OF CONTENTS

Introduction

The most effective children's poetry should exhibit models of those human virtues worthy of emulation. Mrs. Culver has achieved this quality in this collection of verses for the young. Each poem presents a model American or reflects upon an important process in our nation's history. Although these poems are lesson-bearing, they are couched in such lyrical tones as to make them readable and exciting.

BROADUS N. BUTLER
Assistant to the
Commissioner, U. S.
Office of Education

CRISPUS ATTUCKS
Revolutionary War Hero
About 1723-1770
Massachusetts

To Boston City, one morning,
On a cold, mid-winter day,
Came Crispus Attucks, the sailor,
From a voyage of far away.

This mighty giant of manhood,
Just returned from an ocean trip,
Enjoyed the pulse of the city
After leaving a whaling ship.

Sometime before he had broken
From his miserable life as slave,
But chance would soon have him perish
In a tragedy bold, but brave!

He died in the name of freedom
As he led a group that day.
The Redcoat's aim was so true that
At his feet our good Crispus lay!

The soldiers fired at the crowd and
Four more persons lay there dead!
Revolt we must for the freedom
From such worry, fear and dread!

"The Boston Massacre!" cried all.
By that name it's called today.
The townfolks' anger was such that
It was heard for miles away!

11

"We'll build a statue to Crispus
And the four who fell today!
We'll end this threat to our freedom.
If we must, with our lives we'll pay!"

So when you travel to Boston,
For we know some day you will,
You'll see the statue to Crispus.*
It's on Boston Commons still!

---

*Statue to Crispus Attucks built in 1888.

BENJAMIN BANNEKER

Astronomist, Surveyor, Inventor
1731-1806
Maryland

When Bennie was a teen-age boy,
Each household had a clock;
Though in these thirteen colonies
They merely said, "Tick-tock!"

Said Bennie to himself one day,
"If I could make one strike
Would people want to own this clock?
Is that what they would like?"

He found a way to do all this,
Each hour, and right on time,
His clock sang out most clearly with
A cheerful little chime!

Did Bennie stop at this time? No!
So skilled with maps was he,
The President required *his* help
In laying out D.C.!

PHILLIS WHEATLEY

Poetess
1753-1784
Senegal, West Africa

A little girl was sitting
Near her mother's house one day;
Sat list'ning to the laughter
Of the other children's play.

A shadow fell before her,
Past her mother's watchful eye;
Two roughened hands then seized her,
As they choked her frightened cry.

A slave block in old Boston
Claimed this infant of the sun,
A saddened, weakened child with
Not a friend, not even one.

But Lady Luck stood near her;
On her Fate smiled most sweetly,
For Phillis soon was bought by
Kind Mister John A. Wheatley.

She found this life delightful—
None of slavery's pains she knew.
She called her bonds a blessing,
Though such thoughts were held by few!

Her mistress taught her reading,
And she grew so skilled with rhymes
Her poems became so famous
They are read till present times!

RICHARD ALLEN

Founder of the A.M.E. Church
1760-1831
Pennsylvania

The lot of slaves was always
So full of grief and strife,
They turned toward GOD for comfort,
A better way of life.

The slaves could seldom worship
In churches called their own.
They prayed behind their masters;
Sometimes they prayed alone.

In church, one day, as Richard
Was kneeling down to pray,
An usher came and stopped him;
Told him to go away!

But GOD had given Richard
The gift to lead and teach,
The touch to comfort others,
The voice to pray and preach.

So Richard faced his problem;
He knew the answer true;
A church where all might worship
In peace—as Brothers do.

So with a little band of
Free men as brave as he,
His own church he then founded.
They called it A. M. E.

16

Let's explore these letters and
See what they had in mind:
"A" would stand for African—
A certain pride, we find.

"M", of course means Methodist,
The church from which they came.
"E" stands for Episcopal.*
That's how they chose a name!

---

*A church headed by bishops

NEGRO SPIRITUALS

We'd like to tell you all about
The Negro and his songs.
They were his bit of Heaven in
A world of many wrongs.

He wrapped himself in melody,
Rode high upon the clouds.
He talked right to his Savior in
The cotton fields and crowds.

His song might send a message while
He slaved throughout the day,
To say, "We will escape tonight,"
While chanting "Steal away!"

The old were too defeated, but
The younger spirits soared
When listening to the signal of
"Little Children, Git on Board!"

His heart was often burdened but
His faith was ever strong.
He summoned back his courage by
The healing touch of song!

A song is like a mighty torch
That lights the darkest day,
A song can make the weakest strong
Its words might go this way:

"Don't you let anybody turn you 'round,
Turn you 'round, turn you 'round;
Don't you let anybody turn you 'round;
We're bound for higher ground!

Just lift your head up proud-like
And set your sights real high;
Then you will have the courage
To pass Old Trouble by!

Don't you let anybody turn you 'round
Turn you 'round, turn you 'round!
Don't you let anybody turn you 'round;
We're bound for higher ground!

Each person is important,
Each person has his worth;
So put your best foot forward
And walk GOD'S good green earth!

Don't let anybody turn you 'round
We're bound for higher ground!"

IRA ALDRIDGE

Shakespearean Actor
1805-1867
New York

"My son," said Father, "you are young.
Your life's ahead, your song unsung.
Our people live in fear and strife.
We'll ease this pain; enrich their life.

An actor's life is not for you;
You're meant to spread the gospel true."
But Ira's love was for the stage—
He'd loved it since an early age.

So Ira studied night and day;
At last, a chance soon came his way:
"Good day, kind sir, I've just been told
Your need is for Othello's role."

"No room for Negro actors here!
How can YOU play the great Shakespeare?
And even if you knew "OTHELLO",
The role's been filled by this young fellow."

So Ira left for foreign soil;
His dream still bright, his faith unspoiled.
He played his role, held high his head.
"The greatest yet!" his critics said.

He played his role so very well
And he enjoyed such fame
That in the Shakespeare Theatre there's
A Chair which bears his name!

HARRIET TUBMAN

Freedom Fighter
About 1823-1913
Maryland

"Miss Moses" people called her,
For she was very brave.
She opened doors of freedom
To help the hopeful slave.

She led her folk from bondage
On many, many trips;
A gun beneath her cloak but
A prayer on her lips!

Sometimes they grew so frightened
Their bodies quaked with fears.
She nudged them with her gun and
Then wiped away their tears!

She slipped behind the Rebel lines;
A Union spy was she,
She burned their crops and freed their slaves,
Then left to set more free!

SOJOURNER TRUTH
Freedom Fighter
1797-1883
New York

"Sojourner Truth," she named herself;
To journey was her choice;
This dedicated former slave
Of heady, moving voice.

This voice was raised to help each time
That Freedom was the cause.
Its banners high she always held—
Regardless of the LAWS.*

Her strongest plea was always for
The slave just newly freed;
A little plot of land to work,
A chance to scatter seed.

She nursed the soldiers' battle wounds;
She spoke on rights to vote;
Conferred with Lincoln, Douglass, Brown
And other men of note.

She couldn't read or write at all;
Not one word did she know
But she could melt a heart of stone
With "Let My People Go!"

---

*Fugitive Slave Laws

THE UNDERGROUND RAILROAD

You've heard about this railroad;
Its runs were late at night.
The Riders' bags were packed with
Bright hopes—and also fright.

Each station was the home of
A true friend standing near,
All ready with a meal and
A kindly word of cheer.

To be a good conductor,
It took a person brave;
For each who rode this line was
A very frightened slave!

Friend Levi Coffin thought of
This plan to help the slave.*
Fred Douglass, Vesey, Tubman
Both time and talent gave.

We'll hear much more of Tubman,
Sojourner Truth, Fairbanks,
Nat Turner and Longfellow—
To each a vote of thanks!

A song might be the armor on
That road to Freedom's kiss.
A song would keep the spirits high.
Its words might go like this:

---

*Levi Coffin, a Quaker, organized Underground Railroad in 1825.

This train is bound for Freedom—this train!
This train is bound for Freedom—this train!
This train won't carry the weeper,
No dining car or fancy sleeper.
This train's a Freedom Train—this train.

This train is trav'ling fast—this train.
This train is trav'ling fast—this train.
This train is trav'ling fast;
We're headed north; to be free at last!
This train's a Freedom Train—this train!

FREDERICK DOUGLASS
Freedom-Seeker
1817-1895
Maryland

Slaves couldn't go to school,
Like free boys of their day,
Yet Fred upset that rule;
Most clever was his way:

As bribe he took along a sweet
And found one who could teach.
The two then took a seat—
Beyond Old Master's reach!

His master used a whip;
Fred's work was never done:
So he escaped by ship
When he was twenty-one!

He put on sailor clothes
And boarded ship one day;
Then mingled with all those
Who planned to sail away!

Our Fred was free at last;
There was no turning back!
The die had now been cast;
But Fred still felt some lack!

Said Fred, "At last I'm free!
I'm safe to breathe new air,
But something bothers me—
My brothers left down there!

On each one's day of birth,
He lost his ev'ry right;
But HE who made the earth
Will help me in my fight!

I'll meet with ev'ry man,
Each one I know who'd like
To shape a Master-Plan,
A blow for freedom strike!"

Fred met men like John Brown—
With price upon his head;
He spoke in bush or town
To help the Cause, 'tis said.

This man of lion strength,
Our own Abe Lincoln found,
Had vision of great length
And genius most profound!

By eighteen sixty-two,
The Union's plight was grave.
Said Fred, "The thing to do
Is arm the faithful slave!"

Abe Lincoln listened well.
He signed *THE PROCLAMATION!*
"Our ranks," said he, "will swell.
This plan might save the *Nation!*"

The slave laid down his hoe
To join the Union Side.
Though master now was foe,
His fighting turned the tide!

ABRAHAM LINCOLN

Great Emancipator
1809-1865
Kentucky

Abe Lincoln was a poor man's son;
At work until each day was done.
Too poor to read by candle-light,
The fireplace was his lamp each night!

His books were many winding streams
Which took him to the Land-of-Dreams.
His friends weren't only facts and lore,
He found one in a country store!

All great men thrive on dreams, and such,
But seldom lose the Human Touch.
His sadness, humor, kindly heart
Have set him as the Man-Apart.

Yet TIME has called him cunning, kind;
Short-sighted; and a Master-Mind!
Beloved by millions; slain by Hate.
His resting place is with the GREAT!

HENRY WADSWORTH LONGFELLOW
1807-1882
Maine

I'm glad that Henry Wadsworth
Took pen into his hand
To leave behind a treasure
For all in this great land!

He sang of Hiawatha,
The scars in Jesus' hands,
The friendly little town where
The village smithy stands.

He raised his voice for freedom;
Thought each man should be free,
Thought each his brother's keeper
But not by force—said he!

The treasure is enormous—
We're lucky, you and I.
We do not have to dig it;
It's right here standing nigh!

KATHERINE FERGUSON
Founder of a Sunday School
1779-1854
New York

Young Katy's heart was breaking.
Her mom had just been sold;
To leave behind her child in
A world both bleak and cold.

Her mistress said to Katy,
"Now come to church with me.
You're bound to feel much better,
So dry your eyes. You'll see!"

Small Katy dried her tears though
It seemed her life was done,
But she heard the preacher say that
"God loves us, every one."

Thus warmed by God's protection,
She felt no more alone,
For faith is strong at seven;
With hope her eyes now shown.

The War between the States had
Just staggered to an end,
So Kate was free at last though
Without a job or friend.

A hundred years ago in
The churches 'cross our land
The little ones heard sermons
They did not understand.

Our Katy had been caring
For small ones many a year,
So they, of course, had always
To her been very dear.

So Katy had an idea;
A plan in use these days;
A Sunday School where children
Seek God in child-like ways.

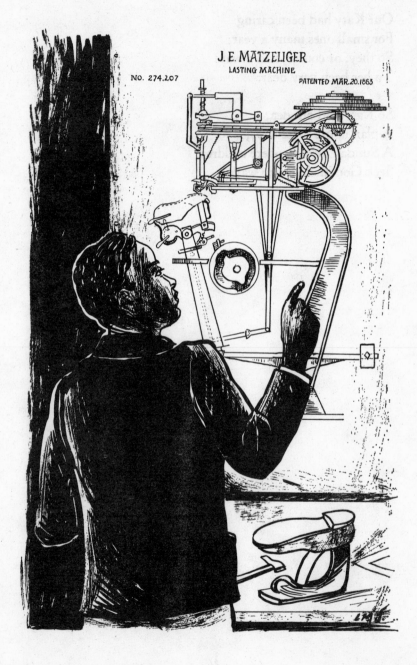

J. E. MATZELIGER
LASTING MACHINE

No. 274,207

PATENTED MAR. 20, 1883

JAN E. MATZELIGER

Inventor of Shoe Lasting Machine
1852-1889
Dutch Guiana

Long years ago, in every land,
The shoes men wore were made by hand.
The work was slow; the cost was high,
So few could more than one pair buy!

This problem stayed on Jan's keen mind.
Said he, "The answer I must find.
I know there must be ways to sew
A shoe, by last from heel to toe!"

He planned his project many days.
He tried at least a hundred ways.
At last he made a fine machine
Whose method's still upon the scene!

ELIJAH MC COY
Inventor of the Lubricating Cup
1843-1929
Michigan

Stop again! This engine
Must have a bit of oil.
Trips would be a pleasure
Without such greasy toil.

Noisy locomotive;
So rusty, never clean,
Must we feed you always,
You creaky, loud machine?

Take us to Elijah.
We'll see what *he* can do.
He will think of SOMETHING
To see this problem through!

"Hello, there, Elijah!
Can you invent a plan?"
"Surely, ev'ry engine
Must bear its own oil can!

"Put this little oil cup
Where it will do the most.
It will oil this engine
On trips from coast to coast."

DR. DANIEL HALE WILLIAMS

Pioneer in Heart Surgery
1858-1931
Pennsylvania

To mend the human heart,
Before eighteen ninety-three,
Yet have the sick one live
Was still a mystery.

Dan Williams made a vow.
"This I must try to do:
Learn to mend a heart
So it will beat like new!"

"It can't be done!" they said.
"You're dreaming! Please don't try!
We never touch the heart.
The man will surely die!"

But Dan said, "Please don't fret.
Someone must make the start."
So he became the first
To mend the human heart!

LEWIS ADAMS

Father of Tuskegee Institute (1881)
    -1905
Alabama

The Civil War was over,
The slaves had all been freed.
One crowning joy of Freedom
Is earning what we need.

Now Lewis, when a slave was
No tiller of the lands,
But tinsmith, harness-maker;
Most useful with his hands.

"Our children need more classrooms,
More people trained to teach,
More farmers, better houses,
Kept safe from hunger's reach!"

A charter granted, Lewis
For Booker T. then sent;
Who did such noble work he
Became first President!*

---

*His official title was principal.

BOOKER T. WASHINGTON

Pioneer in Industrial Education
1865-1915
Virginia

When I grow up
I hope to be
Just half as great
As Booker T.

For proper clothes
He did not wait.
He had no books,
Just one small slate.

He learned and worked
With so much vim,
That Lewis Adams
Heard of him!

With just his hands,
A borrowed tool,
He built the great
Tuskegee School!

DR. GEORGE WASHINGTON CARVER

Botanist
1864-1943
Missouri

Because he cared for plants
He earned the name, "Green Thumb."
"Plant Doctor" also was
What he was called by some.

His fame and wisdom soon
Had spread so far and wide
That George and Booker T.
Were working side by side!

They called him "Savior" when
He stopped an endless toll,
And pushed aside the throne
Of "Old King Cotton Boll."

A kind and gentle man,
A jewel very rare,
He left a better world
For men most everywhere!

DR. W. E. B. DuBOIS

Dean of Historians
1868-1963
Massachusetts

A grand Old Man of Letters,
Proud poet, Speaker, Sage
Most glad we are, and lucky
To live within Your Age.

A truly great Historian,
We point to you with pride,
So few have reached your stature
Or matched your noble stride!

THE NEWEST STAR*
A Memorial to W. E. B. DuBois
1868-1963
Massachusetts

God must have scanned the Heavens,
Said, "It needs just one more light.
I'll place this little star here
To enrich this spot each night!"

This little star was troubled,
Travelling 'cross the evening sky;
Believed his lamp too feeble,
Too unnoticed passing by.

Did GOD say, "Be not troubled;
You shall grow—and more each day;
More constant than a comet's
Streak across the Milky Way!"

And so, we'll search the Heavens;
Search tonight—and if we see
The twinkle of a NEW star,
It's the star of W.E.B.!

---

*Died August 27, 1963 in Ghana, West Africa

HENRY O. TANNER

Painter
1859-1937
Pennsylvania

While Henry was painting
Or modeling with clay,
Most youngsters were busy
And happy at play.

His eyes were engaged by
The sea and the skies,
The roll of the ocean,
The blush of sunrise.

He traveled away to
Bethlehem Town,
Relived the old story,
Then painted it down.

He painted of Jesus,
The Leper's re-birth,
Of Mary the Mother
While Christ was on earth.

He left us a treasure
From heart and from hand,
In galleries here and
His new Foster-land.

ROBERT S. ABBOTT

Founder of Chicago Defender Newspaper (1905)
1870-1940
Georgia

In Robert's early manhood
His people were not news.
There were few ways to reach them
Or tell their thoughts and views.

Said Bob, "I'll start a paper.
We'll print it every week,
The battle won't be easy
To help my people speak."

But Abbot was a fighter.
The battle he did win.
His weapons were some paper,
His printing press and pen!

DR. MARY M. BETHUNE

Founder of Bethune—Cookman College
1875-1955
South Carolina

The sun was shining down on
A cabin dull and gray,
But its household knew a rapture
No want could snatch away.

Old Granny sat and rocked there.
Back-bent from slave days past.
She smiled and sang so softly,
"Thank God, we're free at last!"

The hut was small but twenty,
Would call it home always.
They worked the cotton fields and
To God they gave true praise.

But Mary had a craving,
A great and driving need;
To go to school like others;
Work hard and learn to read!

She walked five miles to school, but
Before she went to bed,
She taught the other children
Just what she heard and read!

She knew what she must do now:
She'd gather God's Black Pearls,
And help improve their chances;
She'd start a school for girls!

One happy day she welcomed
Five girls, her own small son,
Surprising those who'd warned her,
"My child, this can't be done!"

When students lacked tuition;
For shops were closed and still,
A presidential letter*
Brought Mary's drive and skill.

Her kind of dedication
Comes once in many years.
Her deeds made us so grateful
They left no room for tears!

---

*President Franklin Delano Roosevelt appointed her the head of National
Youth Administration for Negro Colleges.

DR. CARTER G. WOODSON

Father of Negro History
1875-1950
Virginia

To poor and humble farmers,
Was born near Christmas Night,
A little son whose star would
Shine with a steady light.

He worked beside his brothers,
Gave many hours of toil,
But constant crops, without rest,
Left little in the soil.

The coal mines in Virginia
Is where he went, we find;
Yet all the while he hungered
For books to feed the mind!

At twenty, when most young men
With school were done and through,
Our Carter started High School—
Did four years in just two!

A teacher, Dean of College,
Professor, Ph.D.,
A man of many honors—
Yet still distressed was he!

For though he'd searched for decades
On every printed page,
The gifts his people gave all
Were missing from each AGE!

Some tell a tale with pictures,
Like tribes who live out West;
The Totem Pole by others,
To tell their story best.

Egyptians wrote with chisels;
Still others used a cave
To leave a lasting story
Of heroes good and brave.

To tell about *his* people,
Of small and great renown,
Our Carter scanned the AGES,
Then wrote THEIR story down!

RALPH BUNCHE

Nobel Peace Prize Winner (1955)
Michigan
1904-

Since dawn broke on the planet earth
To nurture man from day of birth,
It seems that men can't get along;
"More space! More wealth!" has been their song!

It's been no different in our day;
For Peace we still have need to pray.
War storms had formed above the East,
Were raging like an angry beast.

So Ralph was sent to distant lands;
An olive branch held in his hands.
From his great wisdom kept in store
The seeds of Peace he sowed once more!

ROLAND HAYES

Singer
1887-
Georgia

When Roland sang at concerts,
He sang of things most dear,
His tones brought smiles of pleasure,
Sometimes a joyful tear.

He sang of Negro folkways,
And sang them from his heart.
He showed the world their beauty
When no one called them Art.

He sang to many people
In distant place and clime,
With voice as true as crystal,
As golden as a chime!

JOEL A. ROGERS
Historian
1883-
Jamaica, B.W.I.

Our country gives a home to
Great throngs from other lands;
Though here from distant places,
All know their mother lands.

Not so, the Afro-youngster;
His name's locked in the Past,
His mother-tongue forgotten,
Long sealed in lands most vast.

Yet, Joel, when a child, sought
The key in prose and rhyme,
"Just who am I, and where are
My roots; my place in Time?"

His elders said to him, "Child,
Why fret of long ago?
Be happy! This is your home,
The only one you know!

Your Fathers helped to build it
With sweat, hard work and blood;
Yet faithful, loyal always,
Come famine, feast or flood!"

But Joel could not give up;
The puzzle must be solved.
The Past he must uncover,
His thirst for Truth dissolved!

He haunted all the archives;
In Europe much was learned.
His search was long, untiring—
And yet his thirst still burned!

His travels spanned two oceans.
He saw his Fatherland!
He watched the curtain rise on
A pageant old and grand!

This saga he recorded:
The Black Man's skills and schemes,
His gifts, his goals and glory,
His drives, desires and dreams.

WILLIAM LEO HANSBERRY

Historian of Ancient Africa
1894-1965
Mississippi

To spin a tale of Africa
Takes devoted heart and hands,
For she has many cultures, with
Many tongues and varied lands.

For countless years, the writer has
Tried to paint this story down,
To weave into a tapestry
Native wonders he has found,

Now William, when a student, was
Bent on turning back the clock;
To brush back all the cobwebs and
Time's encrusted hands unlock!

He traveled over Africa,
Sought each ancient, hidden tale.
He saw the tombs where Black Kings lay,
Swept aside the time-worn veil.

Bill went to sun-kissed Timbuctu,
Aged shrine of Sages past,
Where at their feet true scholars sat,
Sharing wisdom rich and vast.

He saw the tombs of Sudan which
Nestled under mounds of sand.
Saw stories told on sandstone, when
Kush* was rich and very grand!

---

*Ancient biblical name for Ethiopia

Bill saw the Bronze of Beninland
Cast by masters, then supreme,
The proof of buried cultures, which
Western man had never dreamed!

He's back to tell the story of
Black monarchies of long ago
With missing links of History
Which the world today should know!

LANGSTON HUGHES

Writer
Missouri
1902-

Few can walk in *his* class—
When all is said and done.
One is very lucky
If given Talent One.

Gifted author, playwright
Whose people come to life;
People born to humor,
To music, dreams and strife.

Story-spinner, poet,
A teller of the "Blues";
Have you guessed his name yet?
Of course! It's Langston Hughes!

DR. CHARLES R. DREW

Father of the Blood Bank
Washington, D. C.
1905-1950

Sometimes a very sick one
Needs new blood right away,
Though HOW to store the plasma,
No one could really say.

So Charles R. worked long hours;
At last, he found a way
To store all types of blood and
Have it on hand each day!

The doctor, nurse, the patient
Now give a vote of thanks
To Dr. Charles R. Drew,
The Father of Blood Banks!

PAUL ROBESON

Baritone
1898-
New Jersey

I sat there in the midst of
Ten thousand folk or more;
I felt a little breathless—
Just as I did before!

His music rolled like thunder;
Its spell was everywhere.
It spiraled to the rafters
And took my heart up there!

I came out feeling happy,
As rich as any king.
For I grow ten feet taller
When I hear Robeson sing!

MARIAN ANDERSON

Pennsylvania
1908-

A small brown girl began to sing
On a Sunday fair.
It seemed a lovely angel-voice
Soothing each one there.

For surely Heaven sent this voice,
Precious as sunrise
To bless us with its melody,
Lift us to the skies!

She's sung before the young, the old,
Statesman, workman, king—
For everybody listens, when
She begins to sing!

MAHALIA JACKSON
Gospel Singer
Alabama
1911-

She stood before the multitude,
Serene, her spirit glowing;
The melody began to swell—
A mighty river flowing!

With her, we LIVED her songs of Peace,
Of Faith, great Hope and Pity,
With her we traveled down that road
To *THE ETERNAL CITY.*

We laid aside our cares and woes,
"Moved Up a Little Higher."
We reached "The Upper Room" where HE
Cleansed us with gentle fire.

For when Mahalia sings to us
The dear, beloved Story,
The joys we live, along with her,
Mount very close to glory!

JOE LOUIS
Boxing Champion
Alabama
1914-

Let's give a hand to Joe now—
The toast of young and old,
Called Mighty Brave Brown Bomber,
Unspoiled by fame or gold.

A finer sportsman never
Has put on boxing gloves,
Still idol of great millions,
Ex-champ the whole world loves!

Song* To JACKIE ROBINSON
*Baseball Hall of Fame***
Cairo, Georgia
1919-

The crowd was very still, but tense,
"Play ball!" came Umpire's cry.
Though Jackie stood there poised and set,
He felt alone and shy.

This mood passed over very soon,
For Jackie loved to play.
At first he missed a few, but then
He hit and raced away!

---

*[We sing the last line of each stanza three times (as the refrain)]
**January 22, 1962

Beloved "Bum" he now became,
Our man from far out West.
He helped his team win, many times;
Retired with baseball's best!

Our Jackie played the game so well,
Made such a worthy name,
That he was later chosen for
The Baseball Hall of Fame!

JESSE OWENS
Olympic Star of 1936
1913-
Alabama

Our boys had crossed the ocean,
For good old U. S. A.,
To win Olympic honors,
Earn glory there each day.

So Jesse ran like lightning,
To bring his country fame!
The joy was loud, unchained and
Threw halos 'round his name.

Was this his only effort,
Or Jesse's grandest deed?
He's earned a greater glory
By helping youth in need!

WILMA RUDOLPH
Olympic Star
1940-
Tennessee

Her friends all call her, "Skeeter,"
Though Wilma is her name.
We'll hear the story now of
This "Speed Queen's" flight to fame!

Olympic games were on, but
Because of many things,
Our spirits dragged the ground til
Swift Wilma's toes took wings:

She ran and won a medal,
Then soon she ran once more,
To win that next race also
Just like she'd done before!

She won her third and last one!
Will wonders ever cease?
I guess she's running yet like
A deer against the breeze!

MARTIN LUTHER KING

Peaceful Warrior for Civil Rights; Nobel Peace Prize Winner
1929-
Georgia

God made this world a garden
Abundant, green and good.
Told Man, "Go walk with Mercy
In Peace and Brotherhood!"

But somewhere in his journeys
Man strayed far from the path,
With Brother fighting Brother,
And sinking low in wrath!

King shares the Peace that Ghandi
Held closely to his heart,
Feels GOD condemns all malice
That keeps men far apart!

For Martin knows GOD gives from
HIMSELF a little spark.
So in his strides toward justice
In peace he does embark!

TO THE FREEDOM RIDERS

The path that leads to Freedom
Was lighted long ago.
Sojourner grasped a spark and
Then fanned it to a glow!

Fred Douglass watched his candle
With guarded, loving eyes.
His faith as strong and sure as
Tomorrow's new sunrise!

This road was walked by Tubman;
She met Fred on her way,
As each one helped the other,
Both dreamed of Freedom Day!

There are many kinds of Freedom:
To study, work, and play,
To walk God's earth and proudly,
Leave Fear behind each day.

Though Freedom's torch may flicker,
No one can kill its sparks!
'Twas fanned by one brave seamstress
Whose name is Rosa Parks!

She passed it to another—
Brave Martin Luther King
Who leads *ALL* creeds in battle
To make true freedom ring!

JAMES MEREDITH
Courageous Student*
1933-
Mississippi

A lonely figure strode on,
Alone, yet midst a crowd;
Though hearing jeers of hundreds,
His head was still unbowed!

Alone is not the right word—
For millions walked with him,
Some fearful, others joyous;
Some eyes with tears grew dim.

Like James, take heart, my children.
Most hurdles you can mount;
For soon, good men who falter
Will stand up for the count!

Like James, work hard, my children.
The weak can always hate,
Your education's one thing
No foe can dissipate!

---

*Graduated August 1963, from University of Mississippi.

MY BROTHER

Christian, Hindu, Little Jew,
What does Brother mean to you?
Must his worship be the same?
Should he wear your own last name?

No, my Brother's home may be
Near the rolling China Sea,
In a frozen Polar Land,
On a patch of desert sand.

He may rest his sleepy head
Near a Congo River bed,
Palm trees etched against the skies—
Many more call Paradise.

Each is sometimes happy, sad,
Sometimes noble, humble, bad.
Whether home, at prayer or school,
Each strives toward his Golden Rule!

How can tongue, or time, or place
Separate the Human Race?
HE who made us great and small
Made us Brothers—one and all!